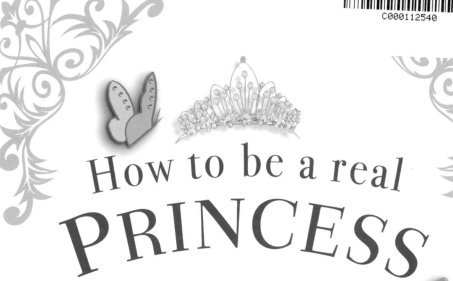

How to be a real
PRINCESS

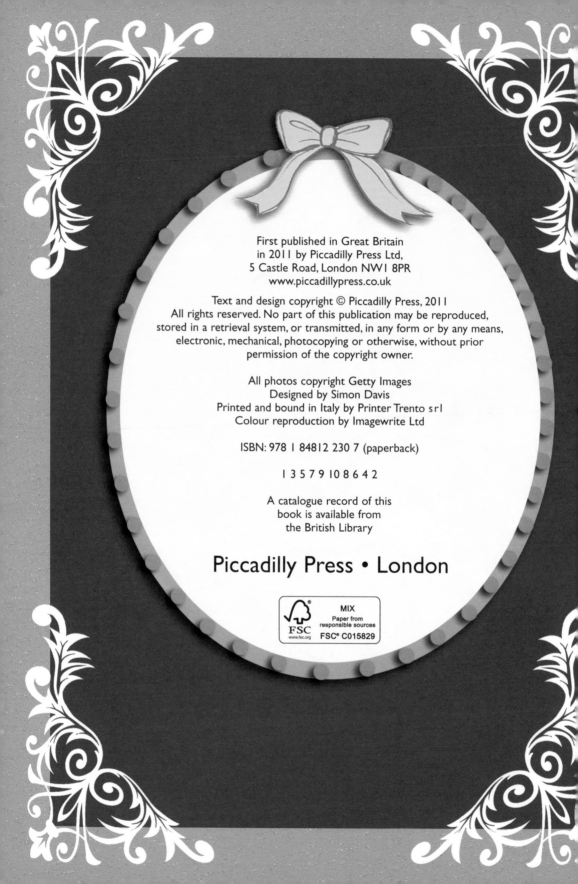

First published in Great Britain
in 2011 by Piccadilly Press Ltd,
5 Castle Road, London NW1 8PR
www.piccadillypress.co.uk

All photos copyright Getty Images
Designed by Simon Davis
Printed and bound in Italy by Printer Trento srl
Colour reproduction by Imagewrite Ltd

ISBN: 978 1 84812 230 7 (paperback)

1 3 5 7 9 10 8 6 4 2

A catalogue record of this
book is available from
the British Library

Piccadilly Press • London

FSC
www.fsc.org

MIX
Paper from
responsible sources
FSC® C015829

How to be a real
PRINCESS

Piccadilly Press • London

A real-life Cinderella

What do you think a real princess should be like? Kate Middleton is pretty perfect. She is beautiful, clever, graceful. But Kate hasn't always been a princess – she was born into an ordinary family who run a company selling items like balloons and paper cups for parties. Kate only became royal when she married the Queen's grandson, Prince William, at Westminster Abbey on 29 April 2011. On that day, Kate's life changed forever.

Doing her duty

Becoming a real princess means that Kate has a new full-time job! As a member of the royal family, Kate will no longer be able to spend her time as she likes. Prince William has an office team at St James's Palace in London who keep a diary noting all the events he has to go to, and they will also do this for Kate. Her days will become a whirl of visiting people and places all over Britain, and abroad. It will be fun, but tiring too.

If you were a real princess what would you want your diary of duties to look like? Design the cover here by writing, drawing and sticking on whatever you like.

Diary

Royal Relations

Kate has a younger sister, Pippa, and a younger brother, James, as well as her mother and father, Carole and Michael. But she now has lots of royal relations. Here is how Kate fits into the British Royal Family tree:

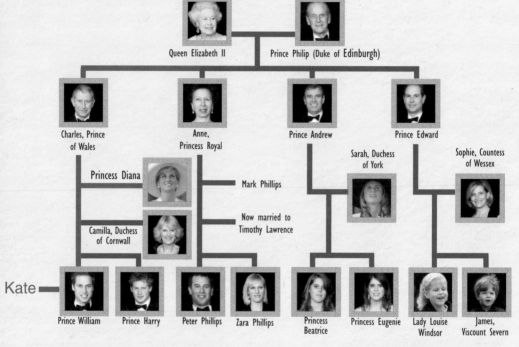

A special symbol

From medieval times, noble people like princesses and knights have all had their own picture, called a coat of arms, to display on things like flags and suits of armour. Now Kate's family have their own coat of arms too, which looks like this:

Draw your own family tree here.

If you were a real princess, what would you want your coat of arms to look like?

Design it here.

This is what some of the traditional colours and pictures on coats of arms mean:

- Gold – generosity
- Silver/white – peace
- Red – fighting strength
- Blue – truth/loyalty
- Green – hope/joy
- Purple – royalty/justice
- Orange – noble hopes

- Lion/unicorn – courage & strength
- Flaming torch – cleverness
- Sword – justice & honour
- Sun – glory & splendour
- Tree – life & death
- Trumpet – ready for battle
- Wings – swiftness & protection

A Princess at Home

Kate and Prince William don't live in a fairy tale castle or have a moat and a drawbridge. Their home in London is an apartment in Kensington Palace – a grand mansion in London which has belonged to the British Royal Family for nearly 400 years. Kensington Palace is open at certain times to visitors, so you can go and look around inside – but visitors are not allowed into the section that is reserved for the family.

Fast fact

Kate's royal titles are: Her Royal Highness Princess William Arthur Philip Louis, Duchess of Cambridge, Countess of Strathearn, and Baroness Carrickfergus. She doesn't use a surname, but it is actually Mountbatten-Windsor.

A gorgeous garden

Kensington Palace has a beautiful 'sunken garden' filled with a pond and fountain at the centre, surrounded by flowers.

If you were a princess, which flowers would you want in your garden?

- ☑ Roses
- ☑ Lily of the Valley
- ☐ Pansies
- ☐ Sweet Peas

- ☑ Lilies
- ☑ Sunflowers
- ☑ Tulips
- ☑ Daffodils

A princess in private

Kate and William will spend most of their time at their house on the island of Anglesey in Wales. This is where Prince William is stationed for his work as a helicopter search and rescue pilot in the Royal Air Force. The couple's house is a normal-looking white-washed cottage set in a tucked-away spot far from prying eyes.

A princess should have the perfect bedroom for pampering herself and dreaming in.

If you were a real princess, what would you want your bedroom to look like? Draw it here. You could put Kate in the picture with you, if you like.

King and Queen in Waiting

Many princesses never get to be queen (like Princess Eugeni[e] and Beatrice) – but Kate Middleton probably will! After Quee[n] Elizabeth and Prince Charles, it will be Prince William's turn o[n] the throne. He will be King William V and Kate will be Quee[n] Catherine.

As a coupl[e]

Kate and Princ[e] William's first officia[l] appearance togethe[r] was a ceremon[y] to name a new lifeboat on the islan[d] of Anglesey. Princ[e] William gave [a] speech before Kat[e] followed the traditio[n] of opening a bottle of champagne over the lifeboa[t]

Fast fact

Kate learned how to sing the Welsh National Anthem in Welsh for the lifeboat naming ceremony.

Beautiful bouquets

Kate will receive many beautiful bouquets at the important events she will attend. If you were a princess, what sort of bouquet would you like to be given?

Draw it above.

Mingling with the stars

As the future queen, Kate will be called on to attend many special events such as posh lunches and dinners, gala nights at the theatre, charity balls, and so on. She will get to meet important people like world leaders, and famous stars like actors, pop singers and sports champions.

If you were a princess, who would you like to meet and why? Write your thoughts below.

A Princess for the People

It won't just be the rich and famous who are lucky enough to meet Kate. Her royal duties will take her all over Britain, visiting places like schools, hospitals, sports centres and exhibitions, where ordinary people will have the chance to see her and maybe talk to her too.

Say cheese!

If you do get to meet Kate one day, don't forget to ask someone to take a photograph! Stick it here – or if you can't wait, draw what you think the photo would look like instead.

Offer Kate an invitation

Would you like Kate to visit your school? Write her a letter here explaining why you would like her to come, what you would show her, and why she would enjoy it.

Invitation

A Champion for Charity

One of Kate's most important duties as a princess is to support charities and their efforts to aid people, animals and the environment. Charities can only keep their good

work going if people give them money and time as volunteers. If Kate takes an interest in a charity's work it will bring that charity attention and not only raise more money, but also inspire people to help.

A model student

In 2002, before Kate and Prince William were a couple, Kate took part in a university fashion show to raise money for the charity Oxfam. She modelled a dress made by a friend. When Prince William saw her on the catwalk, he made up his mind to ask her out!

Fast fact

The dress Kate wore in the charity fashion show cost £30 to make. In 2011 it sold at an auction for a whopping £78,000!

Choose a charity

Kate can decide to become the official supporter of a charity – a patron. If you were a princess, which sort of charity would you choose to be a patron of?

Try this quick quiz to help you make up your mind.

Which of these makes you happiest?
A) Taking care of your pets or being outdoors
B) Playing with your or your mates' younger brothers or sisters
C) Cheering up someone who is ill, old and lonely, or worse off than you
D) Taking on a challenge like a sponsored walk or a car boot sale

When you doodle, what are you most likely to draw?
A) Flowers
B) Smiley faces
C) Hearts and kisses
D) Stars

Which of these colours do you like best?
A) Green, orange or brown
B) Red, yellow or blue
C) Pink, purple or white
D) Silver, gold or black

If you answered:
Mostly As:
You're an animal-loving green goddess, and should support charities which help creatures, conservation and the environment.
Mostly Bs: You're full of energy, enthusiasm and fun, and should support charities which help children.
Mostly Cs: You're kind, caring and compassionate, and should support charities which help the sick, the elderly, or the homeless.
Mostly Ds: You've got drive and determination and like thinking BIG – you should support charities which aim to improve life in very poor Third World countries.

Don't Forget Your Toothbrush!

After Kate and Prince William got married, they went on honeymoon in royal style. They were whisked away by private jet and helicopter to a tiny, private, desert island in the Seychelles in the Indian Ocean – the exact destination was kept top-secret, so no reporters and photographers could follow them. They stayed in a luxury beach villa with its own butler, an open-air shower, and a private garden with a wooden deck out over the ocean.

Fast fact

Kate and Prince William haven't always had glamorous, luxury holidays. As teenagers, they each roughed it on a trip to a poor part of Chile in South America, to help the local people while sharing very basic conditions with them.

Dream destinations

As well as going on luxury holidays, Kate will get the chance to jet all over the world on royal business. The prince and princess's

first official tour as a couple was across the Atlantic to Canada in July 2011, including taking a trip up to the snowy Arctic to go whale-watching. Afterwards, they visited sunny California in America – the home of Hollywood and Disneyland. It was the first time that Kate had ever visited the United States.

If you were a princess, which places in the world would you like to visit most? If you were lucky enough to travel to one, what would you say on a postcard home? Here's one to write now.

TO: _____

_____

_____

_____

Living in the Spotlight

Life as the future queen is not always easy. Wherever Kate goes, she is followed by a crowd of calling, pushing photographers, all jostling for the best picture. She must feel

under a lot of pressure to look her best all the time. Besides which, being a princess can be hard work and tiring. From time to time, Kate will be so busy with official duties she won't see much of her family. Although being a princess is exciting, it can be very challenging too.

A poem to make a princess smile

Imagine Kate is feeling a bit fed up.

Write a short poem here to cheer her up.

The perfect princess pick-me-up

If you were a princess and feeling a bit down, what would you do to cheer yourself up?

Put numbers in the circles to show your favourite choices.

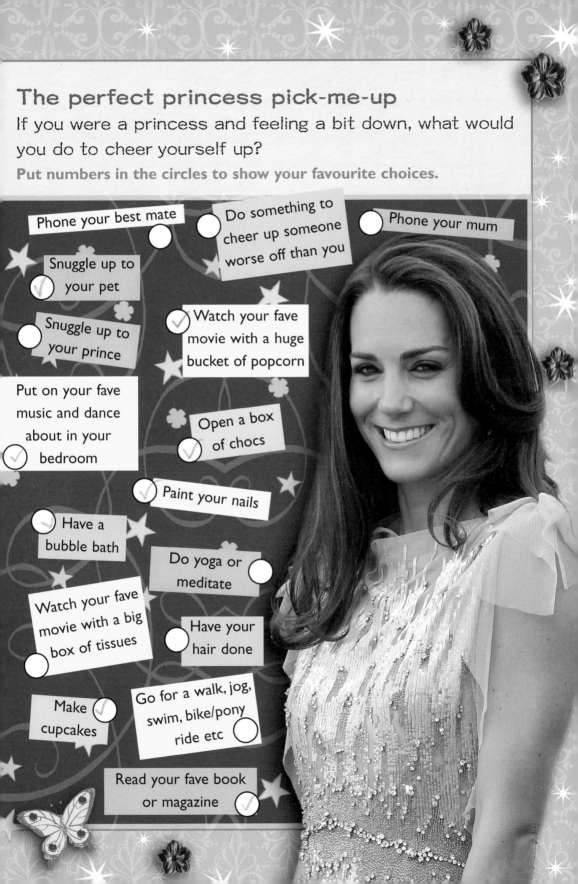

Phone your best mate ○

Do something to cheer up someone worse off than you ○

Phone your mum ○

Snuggle up to your pet ✓

Snuggle up to your prince ○

Watch your fave movie with a huge bucket of popcorn ✓

Put on your fave music and dance about in your bedroom ✓

Open a box of chocs ✓

Paint your nails ✓

Have a bubble bath ✓

Do yoga or meditate ○

Watch your fave movie with a big box of tissues ○

Have your hair done ○

Make cupcakes ✓

Go for a walk, jog, swim, bike/pony ride etc ○

Read your fave book or magazine ✓

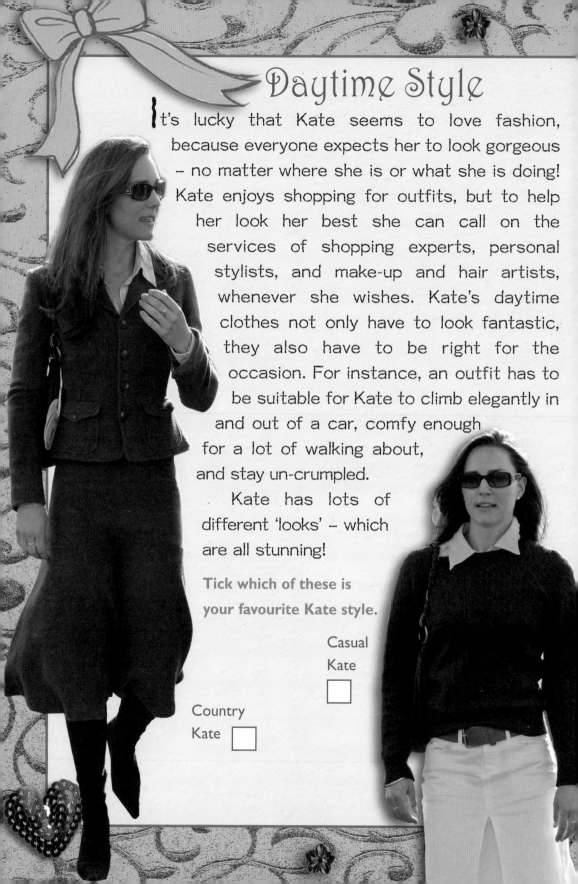

Daytime Style

It's lucky that Kate seems to love fashion, because everyone expects her to look gorgeous – no matter where she is or what she is doing! Kate enjoys shopping for outfits, but to help her look her best she can call on the services of shopping experts, personal stylists, and make-up and hair artists, whenever she wishes. Kate's daytime clothes not only have to look fantastic, they also have to be right for the occasion. For instance, an outfit has to be suitable for Kate to climb elegantly in and out of a car, comfy enough for a lot of walking about, and stay un-crumpled.

Kate has lots of different 'looks' – which are all stunning!

Tick which of these is your favourite Kate style.

Casual
Kate
☐

Country
Kate ☐

Head-turning hats

Kate loves dramatic hats! There will be many times when Kate has to wear one – from high society weddings to days at the races. **Draw a show-stopping hat for Kate here.**

Royal occasion Kate ✓

Evening Glamour

At star-studded evening extravaganzas, all eyes will be on Kate. Everyone will expect her to be the most glamorous lady there. For the evening party that followed her marriage, Kate swapped her wedding dress for a gown that was easier to dance in. Her white strapless dress had a soft, fluffy, shrug cardigan to keep off the spring night chill and a sparkly band to show off her tiny waist.

Give your party dress some sparkle!

Make a sparkly waistband for your party dress, like Kate's.

You will need some round elastic and lots of glittering beads from a craft shop. Ask an adult to cut the elastic to the right length to fit around your waist, and knot one end. Thread the beads onto the elastic until it is completely covered. Then ask an adult to tie both ends of the elastic together so it makes a circle. Just step into it and pull it up over your party dress until it sits around your waist.

Luscious locks

When it comes to her hair, Kate is strictly a no-fuss kind of girl. However glamorous the occasion, she likes her hair loose and natural. However, for her wedding she had a combination style. Below are different evening styles.

Tick the ones you like best.

Be the belle of the ball

If you were a princess, what would your perfect evening look be? **Draw yourself in sparkling style here.**

Dates with Mates

Once in a while, every princess needs time out from her royal duties to hang out with her friends and just be herself. It's always been important to Kate to have trusted friends who she can have fun with, just like everyone else.

Kate's closest friend is her younger sister, Pippa, with whom she shares everything from shopping trips and spa visits to girly lunches and holidays.

Another fun-loving friend is Holly Branson, daughter of the Virgin airlines billionaire boss Richard Branson. Other best mates persuaded Kate to join a group of athletes called The Sisterhood, who were training to be the first all-female crew to cross the Channel in a traditional Chinese dragon boat!

A princess and her pals

When Kate gets time off from being a princess, she can share all sorts of perks and privileges with her friends. Kate can get the best tickets to concerts and sporting events and ask shops to stay open after closing hours so she and her friends can shop in private. Kate and her mates will avoid having to queue to get in to nightclubs too. In restaurants, Kate will be given the very best table for her and her guests.

If you were a real princess, what would be the perfect day to organise for you and your friends?

Plan your dream day here.

Snow Fun

One of the many things that Kate has in common with her prince is that they both love all sorts of sport – from tennis, horse-racing and shooting, to cycling, hockey and swimming. But one of their absolute favourites is skiing. In fact, it was when Kate and William were skiing in the Swiss resort of Klosters in 2004 that they kissed in public for the very first time. Like most of the British royals, they will no doubt try to go skiing every spring.

Swiss Chocolate and Strawberries

Switzerland is famous for its delicious chocolate – but you don't have to go skiing to enjoy it!

CHOCOLATE-DIPPED STRAWBERRIES.

Ask an adult to simmer a saucepan with a couple of inches of water on the stove, then turn off the heat. Place a heatproof bowl into the water and melt 200g of Swiss chocolate inside, then stir until smooth. Line a baking tray with greaseproof paper. Holding the strawberries by their stems, dip them into the melted chocolate, twisting slightly as you lift them out to let the excess chocolate drip back into the bowl, and then set them down on the tray to cool.

You could try decorating them with chopped nuts or sparkly sprinkles whilst they're still soft, or drizzling melted white chocolate over them after they've cooled.

If you were a real princess, do you think you would love hurtling down a snowy slope at speed? Or would you rather sit in a mountaintop café with a deluxe hot chocolate, admiring the view?

You could also go on a romantic snowy sleighride, ice skate on a frozen lake, swim in a stunning outdoor pool, build a snowman, or just relax in your hotel's spa!

Plan your perfect winter holiday with your prince below.

A Royal Christmas

Before she married, Kate always celebrated Christmas in a traditional way with her mum, dad, Pippa and her younger brother, James. But now she is a princess, the Queen will invite her to share the day with the royal family at her country estate, Sandringham, in Norfolk.

As a princess, Kate gets to open her presents a day early! The royal family traditionally open them on Christmas Eve, in a grand drawing room around a 20ft Christmas tree that the Queen always decorates herself. The ladies wear evening gowns and the men wear dinner suits and sit down to enjoy a lavish candlelit banquet.

After breakfast on Christmas Day, Kate and Prince William will join the rest of the royal family to attend a service at a nearby church – they will be greeted by a crowd of well wishers and photographers. At 1pm they will have turkey with all the trimmings for Christmas lunch, and at 3pm settle in front of a log fire to watch the Queen's speech on TV – with the Queen!

Presents for a princess

The royal family are so wealthy that Christmas shopping is no problem for them. If you were a real princess, what presents would you buy? Sometimes very personal little presents – maybe even handmade things – are better than big expensive ones.

Write your ideas here.

For your prince . . .

For your mum . . .

For your dad . . .

For your brothers/sisters . . .

For your grandparents . . .

For your uncles/aunties . . .

For your cousins . . .

And what would you like for yourself? . . .

A Christmas card from Kate

Kate and Prince William will have specially-designed Christmas cards to send to family and friends. If you were a real princess, what picture and words would you want on your Christmas card?

Draw your design here.

A Kate Keepsake

If you are ever lucky enough to meet Kate, don't forget to curtsy and call her 'Your Royal Highness' or 'ma'am' (pronounced as in 'ham'). If you manage to get a photo of her, or if you see a photo of her that you really like in a magazine, why not make a special photo frame to put it in. You will need: an empty CD box, scissors and glue, sparkly sequins and glitter etc to decorate it with.

1. Take out all the plastic and paper bits to leave an empty CD case. Carefully unhook the front of the case.

2. Cut your photo to fit the width of the case. Don't worry if there are gaps at the top and bottom. Use a tiny dot of glue in each corner to stick it into the front of the case so it shows through the outside of the clear plastic cover.

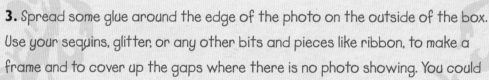

3. Spread some glue around the edge of the photo on the outside of the box. Use your sequins, glitter, or any other bits and pieces like ribbon, to make a frame and to cover up the gaps where there is no photo showing. You could even make and decorate a paper tiara and stick it on the top of the frame.

Fast fact

If you would like to write to Kate, send your letter to her at: Clarence House, London, SW1A 1BA.

4. Put the back of the case upside down and hook the front back in place. Your picture will stand up on its own!

Follow in Kate's footsteps

If you would like to follow all the exciting things Kate gets up to as a real princess, there are several websites that will help you keep in touch.

The official website of the royal family is at www.royal.gov.uk

There is information about Kate and William at the Prince of Wales's official website at

www.princeofwales.gov.uk/personalprofiles/thedukeandduchessofcambridge

There are news updates at www.katemiddleton.com and the official website of

Kate and William's wedding is at www.officialroyalwedding2011.org